D0409338

Who In The World Am I?
Mystery Celebrity Quiz

Lagoon Books, London

Editor: Heather Dickson
Research: Kelly Bradford, Ann Marangos
Additional contributors: Jennifer Steele,
Peter Kirkham, Rosie Atkins
Illustrator: Alex Hughes
Page design and layout: Linley Clode
Cover design: Gary Inwood Studios

Published by:
LAGOON BOOKS
PO BOX 311, KT2 5QW, UK

ISBN: 1899712275

© LAGOON BOOKS, 1997
Lagoon Books is a trade mark of
Lagoon Trading Company Limited. All rights reserved.

Printed in France.

Who In The World Am I?

Mystery Celebrity Quiz

LAGOON
BOOKS

A highly entertaining personality quiz for everyone in the family to enjoy. With the help of ten clues - in order of decreasing difficulty - you have to decide which famous person is being described on each page. Any one who can guess the identity of the person, after reading only half of the clues, is a true star-spotting genius. Anyone who needs to read all ten clues, before guessing who it is, should consider buying a copy of Who's Who!

The clues range from obscure snippets of information to better-known facts and from birth dates to B-movies and previous jobs to personal triumphs. Read each carefully to help you to decide...

... WHO IN THE WORLD AM I?

Whether read alone or played as a quiz, this pocket-sized book will provide hours of amusement - and don't forget to guess which celebrity has been drawn in each of the illustrations. If you can't guess who it is from the silhouette portrait, then have a look at the three pictorial clues.

The answers are in the back, but no cheating...

1   He was born in London, England, in 1947

2   One of his previous jobs was as a commercial artist

3   Early in his career he acted in community theatre and spent two years with the Lindsay Kemp Mime Troupe in London

4   His first band was called 'Davie Jones and the King Bees'

5   In 1969 he made his film debut in the 'Virgin Soldiers'

6   He is an accomplished guitarist and sax player

7   In 1997 he floated himself on NASDAQ

8   His nickname is 'The Thin White Duke'

9   He recorded a duet with Mick Jagger

10   He is also known as 'Ziggy Stardust'

1 She was born in London, England, in 1933

2 She spent two years at the Royal Academy of Dramatic Art

3 Her film debut was in 1951 in 'Lady Godiva Rides Again'

4 Her ex-boyfriends include Warren Beatty and Ryan O'Neal

5 Just before her fiftieth birthday she posed nude for 'Playboy'

6 Her latest biography is called 'Second Act'

7 She has launched a perfume called 'Spectacular'

8 In the 1980s, her fourth husband, Peter Holm, sued her for alimony

9 Her sister is a well-known novelist

10 She is most famous for playing super-bitch Alexis in the TV show 'Dynasty'

He was born in Pittsburgh, Pennsylvania, in 1928

1

In 1968 he nearly died after being shot by a feminist actress who had appeared in one of his films

2

He directed a music video for 'The Cars'

3

From 1969 until he died, he published 'Interview', a magazine about celebrities

4

His film credits include 'Chelsea Girls' and 'Trash'

5

In 1994 a museum of his work was opened in Pittsburgh, USA

6

He organised a touring show in 1966 called 'Exploding Plastic Inevitable'

7

He produced a series of silk-screen prints of Marilyn Monroe and Elvis Presley

8

His New York studio was called 'The Factory'

9

Among his most famous works are his paintings of Campbell's soup cans and Coca-Cola bottles

10

1 He was born in 1933; his mother was a charwoman and his father a fish-porter

2 His childhood was spent in poverty in South London

3 During World War II he was evacuated to Norfolk, England

4 In his 1992 autobiography he revealed that he had a brother in a mental institution

5 He played an agent called Harry Palmer in a series of spy films

6 Maurice Micklewhite is his real name

7 He owns five restaurants in London and one in Miami

8 His accolades include a Golden Globe for 'Educating Rita'

9 He is best known for playing the Cockney wide-boy 'Alfie'

10 His stage name is a tribute to his favourite film, 'The Caine Mutiny'

1   He was born in 1920

2   As a child, he was a promising athlete, enjoying football, swimming and mountain climbing

3   He was once a member of an experimental theatre group

4   'Marvel Comics' published a biography of him in 1983

5   He speaks eight languages

6   'Time' magazine named him 'Man of the Year' in 1994

7   When he was 61 years old, an assassination attempt left him with serious injuries

8   His real name is Karol Joseph Wojtyla

9   He is the 265th person to hold his position

10   He is the sovereign of a city that has only 1,000 inhabitants

He was born in Germany in 1879

1

His family ran an electrical shop in Munich, but moved to Italy when the business failed

2

His childhood was spent completing jigsaws and building card towers

3

He was an undistinguished scholar and he failed his university entrance exams

4

In 1901 he was appointed an 'Inspector of Patents' in Berne, Switzerland, and became a Swiss citizen

5

In 1905 he published four highly original research papers

6

After Hitler came to power, he worked at the Institute for Advanced Study in Princeton, USA

7

He declined an offer to become president of Israel

8

In 1921 he became world-famous after being awarded the Nobel Prize for Physics

9

He discovered the Theory of Relativity

10

1. She was born in Los Angeles, USA, in 1926

2. Her childhood was unhappy, and she lived with various foster parents

3. When she was 16 years old she married a factory worker called Jim Dougherty

4. Her early career consisted of modelling and walk-on film parts

5. She studied method acting with Lee Strasberg

6. In December 1953 she was named 'Sweetheart of the month' by 'Playboy' magazine

7. One of her husbands was a famous playwright, another a popular baseball star

8. She was voted sexiest female movie-star of all time in 1995

9. In 1962 she sang 'Happy Birthday' to President John F. Kennedy

10. Her real name was Norma Jean Baker

He was born in Brooklyn, New York, in 1935

As a teenager he sold quips to newspaper columnists

From 1961-1964 he performed as a stand-up comedian

His real name is Allen Stewart Konigsberg

In 1969 he made his directing debut with 'Take the Money and Run'

He married one of his 'What's New Pussycat?' co-stars in 1966

In 1977 he failed to show up to collect three Oscars for 'Annie Hall', preferring instead to be with his jazz band

He once said "If my film makes one more person miserable, I'll feel I've done my job"

He lost his former girlfriend Diane Keaton to Warren Beatty

He started dating Mia Farrow in 1980

1

2

3

4

5

6

7

8

9

10

1   He was born in Germany in 1819

2   When asked why he had remained a virgin for so long, he replied "That species of vice disgusts me"

3   A national park in central Saskatchewan in Canada is named after him

4   He was a patron of the arts, science and industry

5   There is a memorial to him in Kensington Gardens, London

6   Queen Victoria was his cousin

7   He popularised the Christmas tree in England

8   He planned the Great Exhibition in 1851

9   'Prince Consort' was his official title

10 His wife Victoria was the Queen of England from 1837 until 1901

He was born in California, USA, in 1947

During his childhood he suffered from rickets

He was awarded the Heisman Trophy for the best college footballer in 1968

His film credits include appearances in 'Killer Force' and 'No Place to Hide'

He has appeared in many television commercials, most notably for the Hertz car-rental company

He was one of the best running backs in professional football playing for the Trojans and the Buffalo Bills

He became a commentator for various televised sporting events, including NBC Sports (1978-1982) and the Summer Olympic Games (1976 and 1984)

He was nicknamed 'The Juice'

He is quoted as saying: "100 per cent not guilty"

His first name is Orenthal

1

2

3

4

5

6

7

8

9

10

Q ~ 13

1 She was born in 1953 to an affluent family

2 She graduated from Harvard University, USA, in 1973 and then spent three years at Oxford University, England

3 Her education was frequently interrupted by travels with her father

4 Her father's government was overthrown and in 1979 he was hanged

5 For five years from 1979 she was either imprisoned or under house arrest

6 She moved to Great Britain after her release in 1984

7 In 1986, after General Zia lifted martial law, she returned to her homeland to a triumphant welcome

8 In 1996 'The Times' claimed she was the world's most powerful woman

9 Her autobiography is called 'Daughter of Destiny'

10 She became the first female Prime Minister of a Muslim state in 1988

1   He was born in 1935

2   After leaving school he spent a short spell as a miner

3   He once made an application for a police cadetship

4   In 1977 he applied to manage England's football team - and never got a reply!

5   His first name is really John

6   In 1967 he was named 'Footballer of the Year'

7   The footballer Jackie Milburn was his uncle

8   He is an Honorary Irish Citizen and a Freeman of the City of Dublin

9   His nickname is 'The Boss'

10   He was a player in England's World Cup winning side in 1966

She was born in Poland in 1867

She emigrated to France in 1891, where she studied at the Sorbonne

She was both a physicist and a chemist

Her husband, whom she married in 1895, was killed in a road accident

She, together with Becquerel, won the 1903 Nobel Prize for Physics

She was born Marya Sklodowska

In 1898 she announced the existence of a chemical element about 400 times as radioactive as uranium

She died in 1934 as a result of being exposed to radiation

In 1910, with Andre-Louis Debierne, she succeeded in isolating pure radium

She with her husband won the 1911 Nobel Prize for Chemistry for their discovery of radium and polonium

1
2
3
4
5
6
7
8
9
10

1. He was born in Surrey, England, in 1945

2. He was brought up to believe his mother was his sister and his grandmother was his mother

3. He was expelled from art college for playing his guitar during lessons

4. Famous pieces of graffiti in London and New York once declared he was God

5. He underwent electro-acupuncture to cure his drug addiction

6. He won Grammy awards in 1997 for Record of the Year and Best Male Pop Vocal Performance

7. He was hospitalised in 1981 for a drinking problem

8. He formed his band 'Cream' in 1966

9. In 1992 he recorded 'Tears in Heaven' as a tribute to his dead son

10. His solo albums include 'Slowhand' and '461 Ocean Boulevard' and he released 'Layla and Other Assorted Love Songs' with Derek & the Dominos

1   She was born in New Zealand in 1944

2   Her real parents were unmarried and she was put up for adoption

3   She was encouraged from an early age to explore her musical talents

4   She moved to England at the age of 22 to study at the London Opera Centre, a division of the Royal Opera House

5   In 1967 she met her Australian husband on a blind date

6   Her two children are both adopted

7   In 1971 she was cast as the Countess in 'The Marriage of Figaro'

8   At three hours' notice she once took over the lead role in 'Otello'

9   She was made a Dame in 1982

10   She sang at the wedding of Prince Charles and Lady Diana Spencer

He was born in Austria in 1889 — 1

His mother was a peasant, his father a customs official — 2

As a youngster he earned pocket money by selling his drawings — 3

His application to join the Academy of Fine Arts in Vienna was rejected due to his 'lack of talent' — 4

He committed suicide the day after his wedding in 1945 — 5

During World War I, he volunteered for service in the Bavarian Army — 6

His army commander made him an education officer — 7

In 1923 he was sentenced to five years' imprisonment after leading an uprising in Munich — 8

His long-term companion was called Eva Braun — 9

While in prison, he dictated his autobiography 'Mein Kampf' — 10

1   The son of a pastor, he was born in 1853

2   He previously worked as a lay preacher, teacher and salesman

3   In 1886 he moved to Paris to live with his art-dealer brother

4   His brother gave him the money to take drawing lessons in Brussels

5   He said "In a painting I want to say something comforting"

6   One of his early works was 'The Potato Eaters', painted in 1885

7   He spent the last years of his life in an asylum

8   He died in 1890, having shot himself

9   One of his paintings was sold for US$59 million in New York in 1987

10 He is famous for cutting off part of his left ear during a quarrel with the artist Gauguin

She was born in America in 1966

1

As a teenager she had a Summer job picking corn in the fields of Illinois

2

Her education was cut short when she dropped out of her chemical engineering course at the Northwestern University, USA

3

She was discovered by a photographer from a local newspaper

4

Her first film role was in 'Fair Game' with William Baldwin

5

A magazine photo of her with singer k d lang caused a lot of controversy

6

In 1995 she was said to be the world's highest-paid model with annual earnings of around US$5 million

7

She has invested in 'Planet Hollywood'

8

She once placed an announcement in 'The Times' confirming her sexuality

9

Her ex-husband is Richard Gere

10

1. He was born in Portsmouth, England, in 1812

2. As a child, he was sent to work in a warehouse after his father was imprisoned for debt

3. He took a job as a legal clerk and went on to become a court reporter

4. He managed a theatre company that played for Queen Victoria

5. In 1842 he travelled to America to lecture against slavery

6. He edited two magazines, 'Household Words' and 'All Year Round'

7. His last piece of work was the unfinished 'Mystery of Edwin Drood'

8. He suffered a fatal stroke in 1870 and was buried in Westminster Abbey

9. His first novel was 'The Pickwick Papers'

10. Scrooge was one of his most famous characters

He was born in California, USA, in 1937 **1**

He lost his baseball scholarship because of drunkenness **2**

His first name is really Charles **3**

He appeared on Broadway in 'Barefoot in the Park' **4**

Much of his time is devoted to environmental issues and politics **5**

He made his acting comeback in 'Havana' in 1990 after four years off-screen **6**

In 1994 he was nominated for an Oscar for directing and co-producing 'Quiz Show' **7**

He formed the Sundance Institute for aspiring young film-makers **8**

Barbra Streisand was his leading lady in 'The Way We Were' **9**

In 1993 he made Demi Moore an 'Indecent Proposal' **10**

1 He was born in Kent, England, in 1943

2 When he left school he obtained a grant to study at the London School of Economics

3 In the 1960s, 11 boys were suspended from a school in the West Midlands for copying his haircut

4 He was once sentenced to three months in prison

5 His film credits include playing a bounty-hunter in 'Freejack'

6 He went to primary school with Keith Richards

7 In 1972 he flew to Nicaragua to search for his wife's relatives who were missing after an earthquake

8 Marianne Faithfull is one of his ex-girlfriends

9 Eric Clapton once joined his band on stage to play guitar in 'Little Red Rooster'

10 He is married to Jerry Hall

1 He was born in New York, USA, in 1946

2 By the time he was 15 years old, he had been expelled from 14 schools

3 He won a scholarship to the American College in Switzerland

4 After he graduated he enrolled at a beauty school

5 His previous jobs have been as a lion-cage cleaner and pizza-making demonstrator

6 He has written under the pseudonyms 'Q Moonblood' and 'J J Deadlock'

7 He decided to become an actor after receiving a standing ovation in a student performance of 'Death of a Salesman'

8 He has two ex-wives, Sasha Czack and Brigitte Nielsen

9 Early in his career he appeared in a porn movie that was renamed 'The Italian Stallion' after he became famous

10 Watching Muhammed Ali boxing prompted him to write the 'Rocky' screenplay

He was born in 1564

His previous jobs included serving an apprenticeship with a butcher

He formed an actors' company called the Chamberlain's Men

He became a shareholder in the Globe Theatre in London, England

He died on his 52nd birthday in 1616

In 1582 he married a farmer's daughter called Anne Hathaway

He is quoted as saying "What time hath scanted men in hair, he hath given them in wit"

Some people believe that his plays were written by someone else, possibly Sir Francis Bacon or the Earl of Southampton

He owned a house in Stratford-upon-Avon called 'New Place'

He wrote 38 plays, including 'Macbeth' and 'A Midsummer Night's Dream'

1

2

3

4

5

6

7

8

9

10

1   She was born in America in 1929 to second-generation Irish immigrants

2   Her father was a rowing champion and a self-made millionaire

3   In 1949 she made her acting debut on Broadway in 'The Father'

4   She starred in Hitchcock's 'Rear Window' alongside James Stewart

5   MGM released a film of her wedding ceremony

6   She was on the board of directors at 20th Century Fox

7   She appeared in 'High Society' in 1956

8   While filming 'To Catch a Thief' on the French Riviera she met her future husband

9   In 1982 she was killed in a car crash, in which her daughter Stephanie also suffered injuries

10   She married Prince Rainier of Monaco in 1956

1 He was born in Illinois, USA, in 1911

2 In 1937 he made his film debut in 'Love is in the Air'

3 He described himself as "The Errol Flynn of the B-movies"

4 He was once president of the Screen Actors' Guild in America

5 In 1964 he made his final film 'The Killer'

6 His first autobiography was called 'Where's the Rest of Me?'

7 John W Hinkley Jr attempted to kill him in 1981

8 He was elected Governor of California in 1966

9 In 1952 he married his second wife, Nancy Davis

10 He was the first divorcee to become President of the USA

He was born in London, England, in 1947 | 1

His father was a musician in the Royal Air Force | 2

He began playing the piano when he was four years old | 3

When he was 11 years old he joined the Royal Academy of Music | 4

In 1958 he joined his first band, 'Bluesology' | 5

He is godfather to John Lennon's son Sean | 6

In 1973 he became vice-president of Watford Football Club | 7

He married in 1984, but announced he was gay in 1990 | 8

Since 1990, all royalties from his singles have been donated to AIDS charities | 9

He sang at the funeral of Diana, Princess of Wales | 10

1   She was born in Vienna in 1755

2   Her father was the Holy Roman Emperor Francis I

3   Her daughter grew up to be Duchess of Angoulême

4   Edmund Burke wrote of her in 1793 "little did I dream that I should have lived to see such disasters fallen upon her, in a nation of gallant men, in a nation of men of honor, and of cavaliers!"

5   A scandal involving a diamond necklace played a large part in her downfall

6   She married the French Crown Prince in 1770 and became the Queen of France while she was still a teenager

7   The French people disliked her because she was a foreigner

8   On the night of 20 June 1791 she tried to escape to France's eastern border dressed as an ordinary traveller

9   When the poor complained they had no bread to eat she famously responded: "Let them eat cake"

10   She was executed on the guillotine during the French Revolution

He was born to Neapolitan parents in 1899

1

He was forced to leave school at 14 years old after hitting a teacher

2

His annual income in 1927 was believed to be US$105 million

3

He was quoted as saying "I'm no Italian. I was born in Brooklyn"

4

In 1931 he was sentenced to 11 years in prison for tax evasion

5

He was semi-paralysed by syphilis in later life, and died in 1947

6

Lucky Luciano was one of his school friends

7

His activities were monitored by a ten-man police team under the leadership of Eliot Ness

8

He orchestrated the St Valentine's Day Massacre in 1929

9

His nickname was 'Scarface'

10

Q~35

1 He was born in Richmond, USA, in 1937

2 His first name is really Henry

3 His education was cut short when he dropped out of college to pursue his acting career

4 In 1960 he starred in 'A Loss of Roses' - his first and last Broadway play

5 His film debut was in 1961 in 'Splendor in the Grass'

6 He bought the screen rights to the 'Dick Tracy' comic strip

7 He won a Best Director Oscar in 1981 for the film 'Reds'

8 In 1991 he married his 'Bugsy' co-star, Annette Bening

9 He played Clyde to Faye Dunaway's Bonnie in 1967

10 Shirley MacLaine is his sister

She was born in England in 1775

1

Her father was a rector in the Parish of Steventon, near Basingstoke, in England

2

She was one of seven children

3

As a child, she wrote stories for her relations

4

Her novels were set in the upper-middle class English countryside

5

She died aged 41 and was buried at Winchester Cathedral

6

After her death several of her incomplete works were published

7

Recent film and television adaptations of her books have led to a revival of interest in her work

8

One of her most popular novels told the story of the five Bennett sisters

9

She wrote 'Emma' and 'Sense and Sensibility'

10

1 He was born in 1925

2 During World War II he served in the American Navy

3 He made his Broadway debut in 'Picnic'

4 He was nominated five times before winning an Academy Award in 1986

5 He established an anti-drug foundation after the death of his son in 1978

6 He owns his own Indy car racing team

7 In 1994 he was awarded an honorary Oscar for his humanitarian work

8 He has his own range of salad dressings, sauces and popcorn

9 His wife, Joanne Woodward, has worked with him in several films including 'The Long Hot Summer' and 'A New Kind of Love'

10 He acted with Robert Redford in the 1969 film 'Butch Cassidy and the Sundance Kid'

1   He was born in New York in 1962

2   He had a form of dyslexia that hampered his education

3   As a child, he wanted to be a professional wrestler

4   He spent a year studying in a Franciscan monastery

5   He was a keen sportsman and took an active part in school musicals

6   He made his film debut in 'Endless Love' with Brooke Shields in 1981

7   He is a member of the Church of Scientology

8   He has starred in 'The Color of Money', 'Risky Business' and 'Days of Thunder'

9   He is married to actress Nicole Kidman

10   He is best known for his role as a fighter pilot in 'Top Gun'

She was born in 1956

Her mother named her after the mountain lodge where she was conceived

As a child she was often mistaken for a boy

She defected to the USA in 1975 and became an American citizen in 1981

In 1983 she earned in excess of one million dollars

In 1985 she wrote her autobiography

As a goodbye gift from officials at Madison Square Garden, two female NYPD cops wheeled out a custom-made Harley Davidson motorcycle

In 1976 she won her first Wimbledon title in a doubles match with Chris Evert

Between 1982 and 1987, she won six successive Wimbledon titles

Her former lover, Judy Nelson, sued her for palimony in 1991

1

2

3

4

5

6

7

8

9

10

Q ~ 41

1 He was born in New Jersey, USA, in 1915

2 In his teens he won first prize on a radio station's amateur hour

3 Rumour has it that his manager planted adoring fans in the front rows of his concerts

4 His vocal chords haemorrhaged in 1952

5 He made his film debut in 'Las Vegas Nights' in 1941

6 In 1953 he won an Academy Award for his role in 'From Here to Eternity'

7 It is believed he used his mob connections to secure film roles

8 He was awarded the Jean Hersholt Humanitarian Award in 1971

9 He left his wife and three children for actress Ava Gardner

10 His nickname is 'Ol' Blue Eyes'

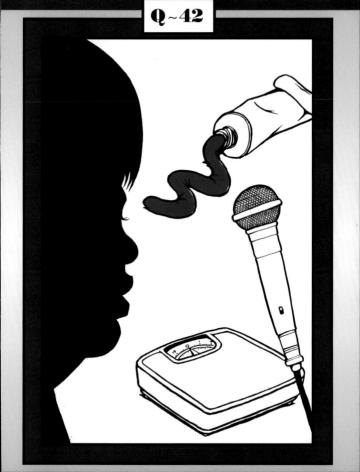

1   He was born in England in 1951

2   He worked previously as a ditch-digger and a teacher

3   He is quoted as saying "I exist in a state of almost perpetual hysteria"

4   One of his early bands was called 'Last Exit'

5   In 1982 he agreed to an out-of-court settlement with Virgin Music over copyright of his early work

6   In 1985 he sang a duet with Phil Collins on 'Long Long Way to Go'

7   His film credits include 'Quadrophenia' and 'Brimstone and Treacle'

8   In 1989 he publicised the plight of the Brazilian rainforests on behalf of the Kayapo Indians

9   He got his nickname because of a striped jersey he used to wear

10   His real name is Gordon Sumner

He was born in England in 1874 - seven and a half months after his parents had married in Paris

1

As a youngster he was an avid butterfly collector - a hobby he enjoyed into adulthood

2

During the 1899 South African War, he worked as a war correspondent for the 'London Morning Post'

3

In 1953 he received the Nobel Prize for literature

4

He once made a daring escape from a prison camp in Pretoria, South Africa

5

The Royal Academy devoted its galleries to a show of his work in 1958

6

His former home in Kent has been turned into a museum

7

He was partial to cigars and Pol Roger champagne

8

In 1995 his family were paid over £13 million for his Chartwell papers

9

He was prime minister of Great Britain from 1940 to 1945 and from 1951 to 1955

10

1 She was born in California, USA, in 1946

2 Her father abandoned her when she was one year old, and she was brought up by her mother

3 She married her first husband, a record producer, when she was 18 years old

4 She has two children called Chastity and Elijah

5 She appeared on Broadway in 'Come Back to the Five and Dime, Jimmy Dean, Jimmy Dean'

6 Early in her career she performed songs with her husband under the names 'Caesar and Cleo'

7 Her solo albums include 'Heart of Stone' and 'Love Hurts'

8 She is a keep-fit fanatic and has released home exercise videos

9 Her real name is Cherilyn Sarkisian La Pierre

10 She won an Academy Award in 1987 for her role in 'Moonstruck'

Little is known about his childhood except that he was born around 1200BC

He was revered as a prophet and was also a teacher and lawgiver

He oversaw the creation and development of systems of worship and a legal system of governance for the community

He was the central figure in the Pentateuch

While tending his sheep he had his first encounter with God

He died at the age of 120

He had a brother called Aaron

He was found in a basket made of papyrus and brought up by one of the Pharaoh's daughters

On Mount Sinai he was given the Ten Commandments by Jehovah

While leading his people to Canaan, he divided the waters of the Red Sea

1
2
3
4
5
6
7
8
9
10

1 She was born in London, England, in 1950

2 Play was stopped at The Oval cricket ground to announce her birth

3 She was a tomboy as a child, and enjoyed climbing trees and making models

4 She was a keen lacrosse player and played in the 1968 British School Lacrosse Tournament

5 Her mother was the wife of a serving naval officer

6 She was a keen rider and shared a pony called William with her elder brother

7 In 1971 she became the three-day eventing European Champion and she represented Great Britain in the 1976 Olympics

8 She is well known for her charity work, for example with the Save the Children Fund

9 She has two children called Peter and Zara

10 Her official title is Princess Royal

He was born in Lucknow, India, in 1940

He arrived in England aboard the SS Kanghi, a wartime troopship

While at secondary school he formed a five-piece group called 'The Quintones'

His real name is Harry Roger Webb

After leaving school he worked in a lamp factory as a credit control clerk

He had a number one hit with a song that was also the title of one of his films

In 1995 he received a knighthood

He is often called 'the English Elvis Presley'

In 1980 he declared his love for former tennis player Sue Barker

He announced in 1970 that he had been celibate for ten years

1

2

3

4

5

6

7

8

9

10

1. He was born in 100BC

2. His parents were members of the aristocracy

3. He was a succesful politician, becoming part of the first Triumvirate in 60BC and then consul of Gaul in 59BC

4. He was a distinguished prose writer, producing outstanding accounts of his campaigns in Gaul

5. He introduced many reforms, including a revised calendar

6. He was married three times: to Cornelia in 84BC, to Pompeia in 68BC and to Calpurnia in 59BC

7. In 50BC Pompey asked him to order his armies to retreat but instead he crossed the River Rubicon into Italy, thereby initiating a civil war

8. He defeated Pompey at Pharsalus (in 48BC) and spent the winter with Cleopatra in Alexandria

9. He was assassinated in the Senate House by republicans, including Brutus and Cassius

10. He is famous for saying "Veni, vidi, vici"

Q ~ 50

1   **S**he was born in Reigate, England, in 1919, but spent part of her childhood in the USA

2   **H**er mother was of Brazilian and Irish descent

3   **W**hen she was seven years old her family moved to China with her father's job

4   **I**n 1955 she married Dr Roberto Arias, who was the ambassador of Panama in London

5   **H**er real name is Margaret Hookham

6   **I**n 1956 she was made a Dame of the British Empire

7   **T**he dancer William Chappell described her as a "rather annoyingly self-possessed child"

8   **S**he became president of the Royal Academy of Dancing in 1954

9   **S**he was prima ballerina of Sadler's Wells and her most famous performances were in classical ballets such as 'Giselle', 'Swan Lake' and 'The Sleeping Beauty'

10   **I**n the 1960s and 1970s she regularly performed with Rudolf Nureyev

He was born in 1946

He married his cousin in 1965

In 1966 he was sent to the Royal Military Academy at Sandhurst, England

He has a personalised Boeing 747 aircraft

One of his homes boasts an international standard golf course in its grounds

He owns 200 Argentinian polo ponies, which live in air-conditioned stables

His name is Hassanal Bolkiah Muizzaddin Waddaulah

He is the 29th person to hold his title

He owns the Dorchester Hotel in London, and the Beverly Hills Hotel in Los Angeles

When he was 21 years old, he became head of state of Brunei following his father's abdication

1

2

3

4

5

6

7

8

9

10

1 He was born in 1889 - probably in London,
   although he sometimes claimed in France

2 His mother and father were music-hall entertainers

3 He made his first stage appearance when he was
   five years old

4 In 1910 he toured the USA with a pantomime troupe

5 His first of four wives was called Mildred Harris

6 He moved to Switzerland in 1952 and lived there
   until he died in 1977

7 He had a home in Beverly Hills known as the
   'Breakaway House'

8 His nickname was 'The Little Tramp'

9 You can find a statue of him in Leicester
   Square, London

10 His trademark was a bowler hat and bamboo cane

1. **S**he was born in Devon, England, in 1890

2. **D**uring World War I she served as a nurse

3. **S**he was made a Dame Commander of the Order of the British Empire in 1971

4. **H**er second marriage was to the English archaeologist Sir Max Mallowan, whom she met while travelling in the Middle East

5. **S**he won the New York Drama Critics' Award for 1954-1955 for her play 'Witness for the Prosecution'

6. **S**he also wrote light romantic novels under the name of Mary Westmacott

7. **'P**ostern of Fate' was the last book she wrote before her death

8. **S**he wrote 77 detective novels, which have been translated into every major language

9. **H**er play 'The Mousetrap' has run in London's West End since 1952

10. **M**iss Marple and Hercule Poirot are her most famous characters

He was born in 1937   **1**

As a child he was obsessive about playing the piano   **2**

During his medical for National Service he pretended to be deaf - the doctor wasn't fooled and he was enlisted in the Royal Artillery   **3**

His big break came after Laurence Olivier employed him at the National Theatre for £14 per week   **4**

While in 'Equus' on Broadway he stopped the show to chastise latecomers in the audience   **5**

In 1975 he gave up alcohol after waking up with a horrendous hangover   **6**

He trained at Cardiff College of Drama and the Royal Academy of Dramatic Art   **7**

He has portrayed Hitler, the Hunchback of Notre Dame and Yitzhak Rabin   **8**

In 1978 he played a ventriloquist in the film 'Magic'   **9**

He won a Best Actor Oscar for his chilling performance in 'The Silence of the Lambs'   **10**

1   He was born in Michigan, USA, in 1950

2   Motown signed him up when he was just 13 years old

3   His first record was released in 1963 and was called 'Fingertips Part Two'

4   In 1970 he released an album, which he co-wrote with his wife, called 'Where I'm Coming From'

5   He campaigned to establish the Martin Luther King Jr National Holiday in America

6   Nelson Mandela said of him 'He is my son, and I speak to him with great affection"

7   In 1972 he toured with the Rolling Stones as their opening act

8   He won five Grammy awards in 1973

9   His real name is Steveland Judkins Morris

10   He has been blind since birth

She was born in Italy in 1820   *1*

Her childhood was spent in Derbyshire, England   *2*

She studied at the Institute for Protestant Deaconesses at Kaiserswerth in Germany and trained at the Institute of Saint Vincent de Paul in Egypt   *3*

In 1907 she was the first woman to be awarded the British Order of Merit   *4*

She tried to persuade Queen Victoria to improve conditions for the British soldier   *5*

Her health failed and from 1857 until her death in 1910 she lived as an invalid   *6*

'Flit on cheering angel' is an anagram of her name   *7*

Her parents named her after the city where she was born   *8*

She established nursing units at Üsküder and Balaklava during the Crimean War   *9*

Her nickname was 'The Lady with the Lamp'   *10*

1 He was born in Ireland in 1854

2 He wrote two collections of fairy stories

3 One of his dramas was made into an opera by Richard Strauss

4 He was regularly ridiculed in 'Punch' magazine

5 His first play, 'Vera', was produced in New York in 1882

6 In 1895 he was sentenced to two years in prison

7 In the last years of his life he wrote under the name 'Sebastian Melmoth'

8 His only novel was called 'The Picture of Dorian Gray'

9 He is quoted as saying: "We are all in the gutter, but some of us are looking at the stars."

10 Stephen Fry portrayed him in the 1997 film of his life

He was born in Louisville, USA, in 1942

In the late 1960s he earned money by lecturing at peace rallies

He starred in a Broadway musical called 'Buck White'

One of his nicknames was 'The Louisville Lip'

He won a gold medal at the 1960 Olympic Games

He famously said "I float like a butterfly and sting like a bee"

In 1978 he became the first boxer to win the World Heavyweight Championship on three occasions

In 1981 he retired from boxing, and was later reported to be suffering from Parkinson's disease

He claimed he was 'The Greatest'

His real name is Cassius Clay

1
2
3
4
5
6
7
8
9
10

1   He was born in Wisconsin, USA, in 1919

2   His Italian father was a member of the Milwaukee Philharmonic Orchestra

3   In 1950 he made his film debut in 'South Sea Sinner'

4   His first name was Wladzia

5   In 1977 he founded a non-profit-making organisation for the performing arts

6   He once worked as a lobby pianist at the New York Plaza Hotel

7   He had his own TV show in the 1950s

8   His final performances were at Radio City Music Hall in 1986

9   His nickname was 'Mr Showmanship'

10   He performed with a candelabra on his grand piano

1   He was born in 1930

2   When he was 16 years old he joined the
    British Navy

3   He has previously worked as a milkman, a
    bricklayer and a lifeguard

4   For 11 years he took dancing lessons from a
    Swedish teacher

5   He was once a nude model for an art college

6   He came third in the Mr Universe 'tall man's
    division' in 1953

7   His first name is really Thomas

8   He made his film debut in 1954 in 'Lilacs in
    the Spring'

9   All of his roles are played with a Scottish accent

10 He is famous for saying "The name's Bond.
    James Bond"

She was born in Germantown, USA, in 1832

She grew up in Massachusetts, USA

Her father was a teacher, a transcendental philosopher and a close friend of the American writer Ralph Waldo Emerson

In 1862, during the Civil War, she served as a nurse in the Union hospital in Georgetown, USA

Her letters home telling of her hospital experiences were published in 1863 and she paid for her first trip to Europe with the proceeds

By the age of 15, she was writing and producing amateur theatricals

She was an active member of the temperance and women's suffrage movements

She never married, and died in 1888, two days after her father

Orchard House in Concord, USA, where she lived, was made a memorial in 1911

Her best-known work is 'Little Women' published in 1868

1
2
3
4
5
6
7
8
9
10

1   He was born in London, England, in 1899

2   Raised as a strict Roman Catholic, he was educated by Jesuits

3   After leaving school he trained as an engineer

4   He once worked for the Henley Telegraph and Cable Company as an estimator

5   He directed his first film, 'The Pleasure Garden' in 1925

6   His wife Alma was a screenwriter on some of his films

7   In 1939 he moved to the US, and became an American citizen in 1955

8   He once said "Television has brought murder back into the home - where it belongs"

9   He had a cameo role in most of his films

10   One of his most popular films was 'Psycho'

1   She was born in Michigan, USA, in 1958

2   Her mother died when she was six years old and she was raised by her father

3   She was educated at the University of Michigan, where she won a dance scholarship

4   One of her previous jobs was working as a waitress at Dunkin' Donuts in Times Square

5   Her first pop group was formed in 1980 and called 'Emmenon'

6   Early in her career she danced with the acclaimed Alvin Ailey and Martha Graham troupes and appeared in the Patrick Hernandez Revue in Paris

7   She appeared on Broadway in 1988 in 'Speed the Plow'

8   In 1985 she sold more singles and albums then anyone else that year

9   She caused controversy in 1992 with the publication of her explicit book 'Sex'

10   She played Eva Peron in the film version of the hit musical 'Evita'

Part Cherokee Indian, he was born in Georgia, USA, in 1936

A serious car accident and a knee injury ended his football career at Florida State University

His former girlfriends include Tammy Wynette and Chris Evert

He built a 'dinner theatre' near Jupiter, Florida, in 1978

He once hoped to become a politician

His film flops include 'Stick' and 'Rent-a-Cop'

He once said "My movies were the kind they show in prisons and aeroplanes, because nobody can leave"

Between 1990 and 1994 he starred in the sitcom 'Evening Shade' and won an Emmy for his performance

In 1972 he posed nude for 'Cosmopolitan'

He had a much-publicised divorce from second wife, Loni Anderson

1

2

3

4

5

6

7

8

9

10

Q ~ 69

1. He was born in Mississippi, USA, in 1935

2. His identical twin brother died at birth

3. When he was ten years old, he won a prize in a talent contest for a rendition of 'Old Shep'

4. He took evening classes to train as an electrical repair man

5. He served in the army as a driver, based in Germany

6. Early in his career he toured South America as the 'Hillbilly Cat'

7. Of his records, 45 have sold more than one million each and he has appeared in 31 movies

8. By the mid-1960s he was the highest-paid entertainer in show business history

9. He owned a Convair 880 aircraft, which he named Lisa Marie after his daughter

10. His former home, Gracelands, has become a shrine to his memory

She was born to peasant parents in 1412

She never learnt to read or write

When she was 13 years old she started to have visions that she believed were from heaven

George Bernard Shaw wrote a play about her

She was tried for heresy and sorcery by an ecclesiastical court

She was pronounced innocent by the Pope 25 years after her death

Her feast day is celebrated on 30 May

She led the French to victory during the Hundred Years' War wearing armour and carrying a religious banner

She is known as the Maid of Orleans

In 1431, she was burnt at the stake and her ashes were thrown into the River Seine

1

2

3

4

5

6

7

8

9

10

Q ~ 71

1. He was born in Philadelphia, USA, in 1949

2. He dropped out of a gymnastics scholarship at the University of Massachusetts

3. In 1970 he joined a rock 'n' roll commune in Vermont

4. He is an accomplished horn player

5. In 1975 he made his first film appearance in 'Report to the Commissioner'

6. He made his Broadway debut in 'Grease' in the 1970s

7. He converted from Methodism to Buddhism in the 1980s

8. He has campaigned about the plight of the exiled Dalai Lama

9. In 1980 he was an 'American Gigolo'

10. He was once married to Cindy Crawford

She was born in Brussels in 1929

1

Her mother was a Dutch baroness, her father an English banker

2

Her childhood ambition was to be a ballerina

3

When World War II broke out she was trapped in Arnhem in the Netherlands

4

Her film career started with a walk-on part in 'The Lavender Hill Mob' in 1951

5

She turned down the role of Anne Frank in a 1959 film, claiming it would have been too painful because of her own wartime memories

6

The actor Mel Ferrer was her first husband; Italian psychiatrist Andrea Dotti was her second

7

The United Nations made her a special ambassador in 1988

8

She played Eliza Doolittle in 'My Fair Lady' opposite Rex Harrison's Professor Higgins

9

In 'Breakfast at Tiffany's' she played Holly Golightly

10

Q ~ 73

1 He was born in the USA in 1895, the first of seven children

2 His mother and father were saloon-keepers

3 As a child, he was sent to St Mary's Industrial School, an institution for delinquents

4° In 1948 a Hollywood film was released covering his life story

5 When he was eight years old, he was playing baseball in a league for 12 year olds

6 Jack Dunn, the owner of the Baltimore Orioles, signed him as a rookie player in 1914

7 He died from throat cancer in 1948, aged 53

8 He was a left-handed pitcher

9 In 1918, he set a baseball record that was to last for 43 years

10 His real name was George Herman Ruth

Salzburg

1 He was born in America in 1956, the sixth of 11 children

2 His father moved his family from the USA in order to protect his sons from being drafted into the Vietnam War

3 After leaving school, he wanted to become a journalist or a chef

4 His film debut was as a surfer in 'Summer City'

5 He was the voice of Captain John Smith in 'Pocahontas'

6 His film company is called Icon Productions

7 In 1985 he was voted 'Sexiest Man Alive' in 'The People' magazine

8 He made his directing debut on 'The Man Without a Face'

9 He was badly beaten up the night before an audition for 'Mad Max'

10 Sporting a kilt and a Scottish accent, he played the part of 'Braveheart'

She was born in Darjeeling, India, in 1913

Her family moved to England when she was six years old, and she was sent to a convent boarding school

She married her first husband when she was 19 years old

Her movie debut was in 1934 in 'Things Are Looking Up'

She was once removed from the House of Lords after speaking up over proposed plans to pull down London's St James' Theatre

When she was 38 years old she received a Best Actress Oscar for her performance in 'A Streetcar Named Desire'

Her last major film performance was in 'The Roman Spring of Mrs Stone' in 1962

Throughout her life she suffered from manic depression

One of her husbands was Laurence Olivier

She was most famous for playing Scarlett O'Hara in 'Gone With the Wind'

1
2
3
4
5
6
7
8
9
10

1. He was born in 1918

2. In order to follow a political career he studied law by correspondence

3. One of his greatest pleasures is watching the sun set with the music of Handel or Tchaikovsky playing

4. In 1964 he was convicted and jailed for acts of sabotage

5. In 1990 he was a political prisoner

6. He was imprisoned on Robben Island

7. In 1944 he joined the African National Congress

8. In 1994 he was elected president of his country

9. His autobiography is entitled 'Long Walk to Freedom'

10. He shared the 1993 Nobel Peace Prize with South Africa's then president, F W de Klerk

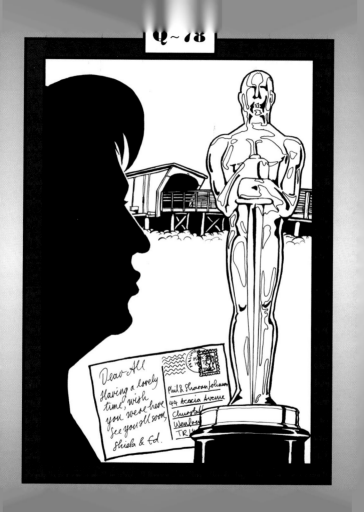

1   He was born to poverty-stricken parents in 1947

2   As a young man, he ran a mail-order business selling fitness books

3   He took correspondence courses from the University of Wisconsin and gained a BA in Business and Economics

4   When he was 20 years old he was crowned Mr Universe

5   In 1976 he starred in the comedy movie 'Stay Hungry' alongside Jeff Bridges and Sally Field

6   In 1990 he became chairman of the President's Council on Physical Fitness

7   He is related by marriage to the Kennedy family

8   In 1994 he played a pregnant man in 'Junior'

9   As well as being an actor, he is a restaurateur and a political activist

10   His most famous on-screen quote is "I'll be back!"

She was born in New Mexico in 1962

As a child, she had two operations to correct her cross-eyes

She dropped out of high school at 16 years old and supported herself by modelling

Her first husband was a musician called Freddy Moore, whom she married when she was 18 years old

In 1984 she played Michael Caine's daughter in 'Blame it on Rio'

Little Richard performed at her wedding

She has appeared in adverts with her second husband, modelling Donna Karan clothes

Her three daughters are called Rumer, Tallulah and Scout

While pregnant she posed nude on the cover of 'Vanity Fair' magazine

She shaved her head to play the female lead in 'G.I. Jane'

1
2
3
4
5
6
7
8
9
10

1   **S**he was born illegitimate in a staunchly Catholic society in 1934

2   **H**er childhood nickname was 'The Toothpick' because she was so skinny

3   **S**he was crowned a 'Princess of the Sea' when she was 14 years old

4   **H**er first film role was as an extra in 'Quo Vadis'

5   **H**er sister was married to the son of the Italian dictator Mussolini

6   **S**he met her future husband while competing in a beauty contest

7   **C**harlie Chaplin said of her: "Out of chaos comes the birth of a star"

8   **S**he stripped down to her underwear in the 1994 film 'Prêt à Porter'

9   **I**n 1962 her marriage to Carlo Ponti was pronounced bigamous by the Vatican

10   **S**he married Cary Grant in the movie 'Houseboat'

He was born in San Francisco, USA, in 1930 — 1

He once swam three miles to shore when a plane he was travelling in crashed in the Pacific Ocean — 2

He has worked as a swimming-pool digger and as a petrol pump attendant — 3

While in the Army, two of his friends encouraged him to become an actor — 4

Universal Studios dropped him after deciding his Adam's apple was too big! — 5

In the 1970s, he set up a production company called 'Malpaso' — 6

One of his ex-wives launched a multi-million dollar law suit against him and Warner Bros in 1996 — 7

In 1971 he made his debut as a director with 'Play Misty for Me' — 8

He has served as the Mayor of Carmel, California — 9

One of his most famous on-screen quotes is "Go ahead, make my day" — 10

1 He was born in 1770

2 Throughout his childhood he supported his family financially as his father was an alcoholic

3 He fought a five-year custody battle for his nephew in 1815

4 He wrote a ballet called 'The Creatures of Prometheus'

5 He was a pupil of the Austrian composers Joseph Haydn and Salieri

6 His only opera, written in 1814, was called 'Fidelio'

7 He died in Vienna on 26 March 1827 and thousands of people lined the path of his funeral procession

8 He is considered amongst musical scholars to be the last great representative of the Viennese classical style

9 He explained his agony over his growing deafness in a letter, which has become known as the 'Heiligenstadt Testament', to his brothers

10 His best known musical works include his 5th Symphony and his 9th Symphony, which includes the 'Ode to Joy'

Q ~ 84

She was born in Los Angeles, USA, in 1962 — 1

She studied literature at Yale University, USA, and graduated magna cum laude in 1985 — 2

Her acting debut was in 1969 on television in 'Mayberry, R F D' — 3

Her first film appearance was in 'Napoleon and Samantha' for Disney, with whom she did numerous other features — 4

She appeared in the television series 'Bob and Carol and Ted and Alice' — 5

She was nominated for an Academy Award for her supporting role in 'Taxi Driver' — 6

From 1974 to 1975 she was in the television series 'Paper Moon' — 7

Her first directing role was for 'Little Man Tate' — 8

She won Academy Awards for best actress for 'The Accused' and 'The Silence of the Lambs' — 9

Her real name is Alicia Christian Foster — 10

Answers

1. David Bowie

2. Mahatma Gandhi:

Clue 1
Prison bars –
Gandhi was seized and
imprisoned many times
during his life

Clue 2
The Rowlatt Acts – passed
by Parliament in 1919,
they gave the Indian
Colonial Authorities
emergency powers – to deal
with so-called
revolutionary activities –
which led to Gandhi's arrest

Clue 3
The spinning wheel –
Gandhi advocated a return
to traditional native Indian
industries and used a
spinning wheel as a symbol
of the simple life which he
preached

3. Joan Collins

4. Andy Warhol

5. Michael Caine

6. Tina Turner:

Clue 1
The 'City Limit' sign –
she released a track called
'Nutbush City Limits'

Clue 2
The 1st prize certificate –
she released a track called
'Simply the Best'

Clue 3
The bullock – her real
name is Annie Mae Bullock

7. The Pope

8. Albert Einstein

9. Marilyn Monroe

10. Woody Allen

11. Prince Albert

12. OJ Simpson

13. Benazir Bhutto

14. Tom Hanks:

Answers

Clue 1
The map of the east coast of America showing Philadelphia – he starred in the film 'Philadelphia'

Clue 2
The rocket – he starred in the film 'Apollo 13'

Clue 3
The red shoe – one of Tom Hanks' early films was called 'The Man with One Red Shoe'

15. Jack Charlton

16. Marie Curie

17. Eric Clapton

18. Pelé:

Clue 1
The Brazilian flag – he is Brazilian

Clue 2
The number 10 shirt – the shirt he is famous for wearing

Clue 3
The hole in the ground – he was in the film 'Escape To Victory' with Michael Caine and Sylvester Stallone

19. Kiri Te Kanawa

20. Adolf Hitler

21. Vincent van Gogh

22. Cindy Crawford

23. Charles Dickens

24. Robert Redford

25. Mick Jagger

26. Margaret Thatcher:

Clue 1
The Falkland Islands outline – she led Britain to victory in a military dispute with Argentina over the sovereignty of the Falkland Islands in 1982

Answers

Clue 2
The test tubes and
Bunsen burner – she
studied chemistry at
Oxford University

Clue 3
Fe is the chemical symbol
for iron and she was
known as 'The Iron Lady'

27. Sylvester Stallone

28. William Shakespeare

29. Grace Kelly

30. Napoleon:

Clue 1
The Arc de Triomphe –
it was built to
commemorate Napoleon

Clue 2
The brandy glass – there is
a make of brandy called
Napoleon Brandy

Clue 3 The pig – in George
Orwell's 'Animal Farm',
the pig is called Napoleon

31. Ronald Reagan

32. Elton John

33. Marie Antoinette

34. Al Capone

35. Warren Beatty

36. Jane Austen

37. Paul Newman

38. John Lennon:

Clue 1
The heart – representing
the album 'Sgt Pepper's
Lonely Hearts Club Band'

Clue 2
The blackbird – 'Blackbird'
is the name of a Beatles song

Clue 3
The guitar –
he played the guitar

39. Tom Cruise

40. Martina Navratilova

Answers

41. Frank Sinatra

42. Oprah Winfrey:

Clue 1
The tube of purple paint –
she played Sofia in the 1985
film 'The Color Purple'

Clue 2
The microphone –
The 'Oprah Winfrey Show'
is an incredibly popular
chat-show

Clue 3
The scales – her fluctuating
weight has always played a
prominent role in her
public life

43. Sting

44. Winston Churchill

45. Cher

46. Moses

47. Princess Anne

48. Cliff Richard

49. Julius Caesar

50. Luciano Pavarotti:

Clue 1
The bowl of pasta –
he is Italian

Clue 2
The football – he sang
'Nessun Dorma', which
was used as the World
Cup song in 1990

Clue 3
The Italian tenor's
trademark white
handkerchief

51. Margot Fonteyn

52. The Sultan of Brunei

53. Charlie Chaplin

54. Marlon Brando:

Clue 1
The couple doing the tango
by the Eiffel Tower – one
of Marlon Brando's star
roles was in the film 'Last
Tango in Paris'

Answers

Clue 2
The motorbike – Marlon Brando is often pictured wearing motorbike jackets and he starred in the film 'The Wild One', which includes many motorbike scenes

Clue 3
The Mafia character – one of Marlon Brando's most famous roles was as 'The Godfather' in a film of the same name

55. Agatha Christie

56. Anthony Hopkins

57. Stevie Wonder

58. Florence Nightingale

59. Oscar Wilde

60. Muhammed Ali

61. Liberace

62. The Queen:

Clue 1
The riding hat and whip – the Queen is a keen rider

Clue 2
The hand of playing cards – the top card is a queen

Clue 3
The Corgi – the Queen owns several dogs of this breed

63. Sean Connery

64. Louisa May Alcott

65. Alfred Hitchcock

66. Martin Luther King:

Clue 1
The map and flag of America in a dream bubble – reference to America's segregated south and King's "I have a Dream..." speech

Clue 2
The ballot box – reference to the drive he led for black voter registration

Clue 3
The Dexter Avenue Baptist Church, Montgomery, Alabama – where King

Answers

was a minister

67. Madonna

68. Burt Reynolds

69. Elvis Presley

70. Joan of Arc

71. Richard Gere

72. Audrey Hepburn

73. Babe Ruth

74. Wolfgang Amadeus Mozart:

Clue 1
The flute – he wrote the opera 'The Magic Flute'

Clue 2
An opera mask – he wrote a variety of operas during his life including 'The Marriage of Figaro' and 'Cosi fan tutte'

Clue 3
'Salzburg' sign – Salzburg is the city where Mozart was born, and where he died

75. Mel Gibson

76. Vivien Leigh

77. Nelson Mandela

78. Meryl Streep:

Clue 1
The bridge – she starred in the film 'The Bridges of Madison County'

Clue 2
The postcard – she starred in the film 'Postcards from the Edge'

Clue 3
The Oscar – she won an Oscar for her role in 'Kramer vs. Kramer'

79. Arnold Schwarzenegger

80. Demi Moore

81. Sophia Loren

82. Clint Eastwood

83. Ludwig van Beethoven

84. Jodie Foster